Out of the
Amazon

The Royal Botanic Gardens, Kew

Out of the Amazon

Photographs of the Brazilian Rainforest by
Sue Cunningham

With text by Ghillean T Prance

London: HMSO

© Text: The Board of Trustees of The Royal Botanic Gardens, Kew, 1992
© Photographs: Sue Cunningham, 1992
© Captions: Patrick Cunningham, 1992

Designed by HMSO: Alison Beaumont

Applications for reproduction should be made to HMSO
First published 1992

ISBN 0 11 250074 9
British Library Cataloguing in Publication Data
A CIP catalogue record for this book is available from the British Library

Sue Cunningham would like to thank the people of Brazil and her family for their help in making this book possible.

HMSO publications are available from:

HMSO Publications Centre
(Mail, fax and telephone orders only)
PO Box 276, London, SW8 5DT
Telephone orders 071-873 9090
General enquiries 071-873 0011
(queuing system in operation for both numbers)
Fax orders 071-873 8200

HMSO Bookshops
49 High Holborn, London, WC1V 6HB   071-873 0011   Fax 071-873 8200 (counter service only)
258 Broad Street, Birmingham, B1 2HE   021-643 3740   Fax 021-643 6510
Southey House, 33 Wine Street, Bristol, BS1 2BQ   0272-264306   Fax 0272-294515
9–21 Princess Street, Manchester, M60 8AS   061-834 7201   Fax 061-833 0634
16 Arthur Street, Belfast, BT1 4GD   0232-238451   Fax 0232-235401
71 Lothian Road, Edinburgh, EH3 9AZ   031-228 4181   Fax 031-229 2734

HMSO's Accredited Agents
(see Yellow Pages)

and through good booksellers

Printed in the United Kingdom for HMSO
Dd 291798 10/92 C50 56-5518 36145

Contents

Introduction

I am happy to write a short text to accompany these beautiful photographs of Amazonia by Sue Cunningham. Many of the pictures in this book were included in an exhibition in the gallery of the Royal Botanic Gardens, Kew, in 1991, and when I saw them there, they brought back many memories of the plants, the people and the environmental situation in the Amazon region. They filled me with *saudade*, a Portuguese word which is impossible to translate into English. The dictionaries often demean the definition of *saudade* by translating it as 'homesickness', whereas it is really a sensation of being reminded of a place, a person or some happening and being given a longing for a repeat performance. I saw in the photographs the Amazon that I know and love portrayed through the eyes of a photographer who obviously has the same sense of concern for the region and a special interest in the indigenous people. I have attempted to bring together some of the facts about the Amazon that are illustrated in these photographs, along with some of my own experiences from twenty-eight years of botanical exploration and research in the Amazonian rainforest.

This is an exciting and important time in the history of the Amazon region. After two decades of environmental destruction, there is now a noticeable change in attitude by the governments of the Amazon countries. Lessons have been learned from the failures of so many projects that were intended to develop the region, and greater value is being attached to the biodiversity of the forest, its role in controlling world-wide climate, and to the contribution of indigenous cultures. We must take hold of this change in attitudes in a positive way and learn to work with the governments of the Amazon countries, rather than against them, because in that way there is hope for the region.

The photographs here are all of the Brazilian Amazon, which covers two-thirds of the Amazon basin, and they show not only the beauty of the forest and its fragility, but also some of the hopeful signs that are emerging for the future of the region and its reconstruction. In fact all the Amazon countries – Brazil, Bolivia, Colombia, Ecuador, French Guiana, Guyana, Peru, Suriname and Venezuela – are now showing concern for their environment, and this is encouraging, because the whole basin holds together as one great and diverse ecosystem. For example, the survival of the lowland areas depends on the management of the watershed areas in the countries around the periphery of the Amazon basin.

We, the author and the photographer, hope that this portrayal of the Brazilian Amazon will encourage interest and positive action in the region that has become so much part of our lives. We must remember that the natural beauty, the biological diversity and the forest peoples that are portrayed so spectacularly in the photographs are still in danger of extinction. Our aim is to promote informed concern for Amazonia. The signs of hope that we see now are a result of the concern expressed by so many people over the last fifteen years and, since deforestation has been stimulated as much by external forces as by the Amazon countries, we have reason to keep alert about what is happening. We now need to use the changes in attitudes of the Amazonian governments to collaborate closely with those countries to assist them towards sustainable use of the region, conservation of its plants and animals, and preservation of the indigenous peoples and their culture.

Map of the Amazon Countries

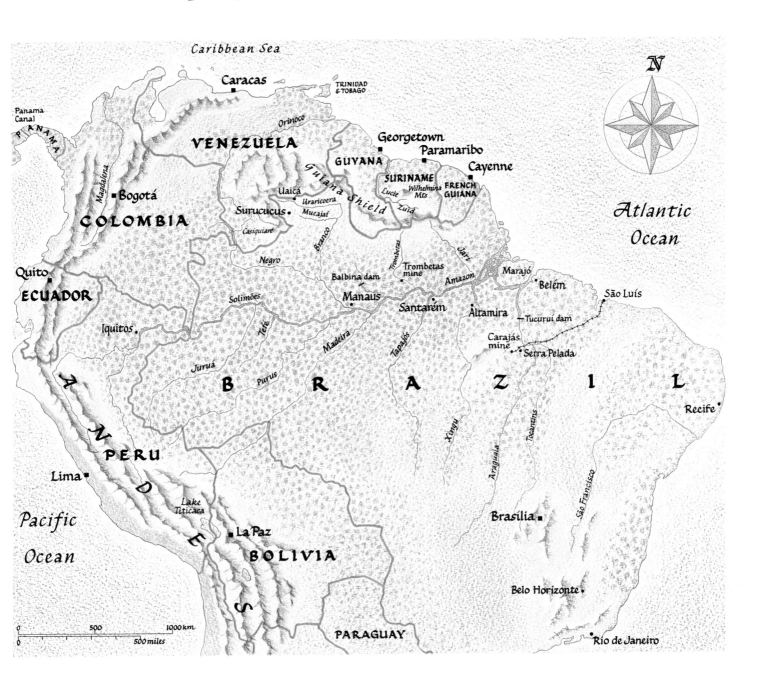

ONE

The Forest

To enter the majestic Amazonian forest for the first time is an awe-inspiring experience. The tall trees with buttressed trunks give the forest a cathedral-like appearance. They form a dense overhead canopy that prevents all but 10 per cent of the sunlight from reaching the forest floor. In the permanent twilight the strangely shaped trunks, no two alike, and the bizarrely contorted stems of the vines begin to play on one's imagination. To the naturalist, this is a paradise because of the great variety of plants and insects which the forest contains. However, for some people, it is hard to bear, and the constant absence of sunlight can bring on claustrophobia. This is unlikely to be a problem for a biologist because there is so much to study and observe, but low light intensity makes photography in the rainforest extremely difficult.

After the rain, the forest can become hot and steamy. Visibility is reduced to a few trees looming out of the mist, tied down by a festoon of hanging lianas. Only at the edge of a clearing is it possible to appreciate the magnificence of individual trees, for here they stand out against the light.

My first visit to the rainforest was to the remote Wilhelmina Mountains of Suriname. After flying in a small plane from the capital, Paramaribo, to a jungle airstrip, it took another two days by canoe along the Lucie River to reach our base camp. Our boatmen were the Djuka, a group of people whose ancestors were escaped African slaves who had returned to tribal life in the forests of Suriname, and even though this was my first river trip, I felt safe and in good hands. On the third day we reached our destination, an expedition base camp on the high banks of the Zuid River. After clambering up the slippery steps carved in the mud of the river bank, I soon became curious about the trees around the camp. One of the first I encountered was a 30-metre-tall tree of *Licania majuscula*, a member of the cocoa plum family that I had just studied for my doctoral thesis. Overjoyed to find a

Licania so quickly, I asked the expedition leader how to collect a specimen of the flowers and leaves for further study. Howard, the leader, said, 'That is easy. We will ask one of the Djuka to cut down the tree so that you can examine it properly.' The only Djuka left in the camp at that time was Frederick the cook. When asked to cut down this majestic tree, Frederick refused. An argument ensued in their Creole language, taki-taki. When the shouting was over, I received an explanation. Frederick did not want to cut down the tree because it would offend his deity, the 'bushy-mama'. He had eventually agreed to do so in half an hour's time when he would have appeased the bushy-mama. He felled this great tree, with a trunk of over 50 centimetres in diameter, all the time chanting a prayer to ensure that the blame was put on the white man who had ordered this unnecessary destruction of the forest, and not on the axeman. A tree of *Licania* is not easy to fell because of its exceptionally hard timber (due to the silica (or sand) grains that are scattered throughout its wood), but Frederick did a magnificent job and the tree was soon horizontal on the ground near the camp and I was collecting herbarium specimens from its crown. However, this is an incident I have never forgotten because on my first day in the forest I learned about the value which some forest people place on their personal environment. It was one of many formative experiences that were to give me an interest, not only in the forest, but in the fascinating people who inhabit it, and in protecting the rainforest environment. On my later expeditions, I have always tried to avoid cutting down the trees and have either used tree climbers or climbed the trees myself.

Unlike the forests of the temperate regions, which are dominated by just one or a couple of species, tropical rainforests contain an amazing diversity of species growing together in low population densities. The largest number of tree species per hectare so far recorded was found in the Amazon rainforest at Yanomono in Peru by Alwyn Gentry, a botanist from the Missouri Botanical Garden. He recorded 300 species of trees and vines of 10 centimetres diameter or more on a single hectare. A hectare which I sampled near Manaus, Brazil, contained 179 species. No wonder no two trunks look alike as one walks through the forest! For the biologist, this diversity is a delight, a wonder and something to be conserved, but to the developer it is anathema because individual species occur in such low population densities that they are hard to exploit. It seems to be much easier to cut down the original forest and replace it with a monoculture of cattle pasture or a commercial timber. However, monocultures rarely thrive in the tropics and areas that are felled often become unproductive because of the poor soil and the number of endemic diseases.

One would think that because of its luxuriant growth and enormous variety of species, rainforest must grow in areas of rich soil. In fact, quite the opposite is true in the case of most of the Amazon rainforest. Some even grows on pure white sand that contains virtually no nutrients. The nutrients are in the vegetation and the fauna, rather than in the soil, and they are rapidly recycled as leaves and branches drop to the forest floor. This contains a mass of superficial tree roots that seek out the nutrients. These roots are often linked to the rotting leaves by mycorrhizal fungi which form a bridge between a dead leaf and a root and therefore assist the recycling of nutrients. I have seen a dead tree with a network of roots of a living tree growing several metres up it to reabsorb the goodness in the dead trunk. The forest prospers on poor soil because of this efficient nutrient recycling system. If the forest is cut and burned, then most of the nutrients are washed away into the streams. Analysis of streams in undisturbed forest shows that the water is pure, almost as pure as distilled water, but streams in deforested areas are full of escaping nutrients that are the lifeblood of the forest.

The tree species in the Amazon forest are only part of the total richness of the plant life there, because rainforests also contain a wealth of herbs, of epiphytes that perch on other plants and parasitic and even saprophytic species that live off the dead leaf litter on the forest floor. These all add considerably to the species diversity of the forest. In the rainforest at the Río Palenque Reserve in Ecuador, Alwyn Gentry and Calaway Dodson found 365 species of flowering plants and ferns in one-tenth of a hectare. In the forests of Costa Rica, Timothy Whitmore and his colleagues found 233 species growing in an area of 100 square metres. An area half the size of a tennis court contained about a sixth as many species as the total flora of the British Isles. The rainforests of Amazonia have a similar diversity of plants. This amount of species diversity is incomprehensible to someone who only knows the forests of Europe or North America, and it is this which is in danger of loss by deforestation.

The diversity of vegetation in the forest is amazing. Even in the poorest sandy soil, there is always a plant ready to take advantage of any nutrients that may be available. The bamboo-like *Gynerium sagittatum* (left), which is used by the Yanomami Indians to make arrow shafts, simply grows through anything in its way. Even in areas of secondary growth (right), the variety in plant forms is vastly greater than might be found in a similar area of temperate forest.

From the air, the magnitude of the Amazon forest (above) becomes apparent. The trees below look like a never-ending green cauliflower that rolls on for hour after hour.

The richness of detail at ground level (right) is extra-ordinary. This enormous garden is very fragile, and in some areas is disappearing at a horrifying rate.

◄ The whole forest is awe-inspiring, but some of the trees are so tall and straight that the tops are almost out of sight. At times, a tree will command you to stand at its foot and look up in wonder.

▲ Wherever an opening in the canopy occurs, dormant seeds on the forest floor spring to life, awoken by the precious rays of light. The forest floor is often dark, and the occasional breaks in the green ceiling point a welcoming finger to the botanical splendour below.

Dawn in the forest often comes gently, the darkness giving way to a grainy mist, which lifts to reveal the undulating sea of the forest canopy. Views such as this are rare, only occurring in high places where the vigorous vegetation has loosed its grip sufficiently to open a window on the trees below.

Around 80 per cent of the total nutrients of the forest are held in the living plant matter. To achieve this, de-composition of dead organic matter is unnervingly rapid. These fungi, although beauti-ful, will help to reduce the tree stump to dust within a few months.

Epiphytic plants, such as the bromeliads which are often found as houseplants in temperate countries, are a vi-tal part of the forest flora. They 'fix' nutrients from the air, providing the forest eco-logy with much-needed bio-mass. They also act as home, larder and nursery to a multi-tude of animals and insects.

The forest flora and fauna are
linked in a complex system of
interdependence. The myriad
birds are essential pollinators
and disperse seeds. They also
supply many of the ever-
present sounds of the forest,
and add sudden splashes of
moving colour to the scene.

TWO

The River & the Rain

Amazonia is the vast wilderness that it is because it is dominated by the mighty Amazon River and its huge network of tributaries. One-fifth of the world's river water flows through the mouth of the Amazon River. It is 6762 kilometres long and its basin covers 5.8 million square kilometres: an area larger than the continent of Europe! The island of Marajó, which stretches across the 320-kilometre-wide mouth of the Amazon, is larger than Switzerland.

There are 80,000 kilometres of navigable waterways, making river transport rather than road transport the obvious way to move goods around the region. Ocean-going cruise ships and freighters can travel up-river to Iquitos, in Peru, which is 3600 kilometres inland from the Atlantic Ocean and is much closer to the Pacific. Navigation is not always easy, however, for in places the current of the main Amazon River flows at 7 knots. The local people know how to read the river and travel upstream in the eddies to avoid paddling against such a mighty force of water.

Montane forest. Far from being uniform, the natural vegetation varies widely through the region, depending on soil type, topography, and the amount of rain.

Not all the rivers of Amazonia are alike, for there are three main types of water. The main Amazon River flows from the Andes, gathering much sediment in the process, and is therefore muddy and looks like white coffee. A billion tons of sediment are washed out to sea each year, which caused one Brazilian senator to lament the loss of land and to seek compensation from the United States, where some of the sediment is carried by ocean currents! This so-called 'white water' is not acid and has a pH of 6.5–7.

The largest tributary of the Amazon is the Rio Negro, which flows from the geologically ancient sandy soils of the Guiana shield. As a result, it is a black water river, which is so dark that if one stands in the water up to the knees one's feet are obscured! This is because of the quantity of dissolved plant material (humic matter) that it contains, just as we find in streams coming from the peat bogs of the British Isles. As a result of this humic matter, the black water rivers are quite acid, with a pH of about 4. There is 26.6 mg/litre of humic matter in the Rio Negro and only 14.1 in the Amazon River.

Three of the large northern-flowing tributaries in the Amazon, the rivers Tocantins, Xingu and Tapajós, represent the third water type: clear or crystalline water. They flow from the rocky savannahs of central Brazil and have neither much sediment nor much humic matter (2.36 mg/litre). The Tapajós River ecosystem is now severely disrupted by the Tucuruí hydroelectric dam, currently the largest dam in the Amazon region.

The different water types influence the flora and fauna which live in the rivers and along their flood plains. Many trees which grow in areas flooded by black water, called *igapó* in Brazil, do not grow in the white water areas (called *várzea* forest) and vice versa. Life in the vast floodplains of the major rivers is dominated by the rise and fall of the water level of the rivers. In the rainy season, the rivers fill and flood over their banks into the *várzea* forest and the *igapó*. In the dry season, the water level drops and the trees are on dry land. The difference between the low and high levels of the river at Manaus harbour in an average year is 11 metres; the greatest recorded difference was 15.5 metres in 1990, when the lowest level ever was recorded in the dry season and the high level was almost a record.

One of the most interesting experiences in Amazonia for a biologist is to take a canoe at the height of the flood season and to paddle among the crowns of the trees, whose trunks go down 10 metres or more underwater. This is the time to observe closely the plant and insect life in these trees, many of which fruit at the peak of the flood so that their seeds fall into the water and are dispersed by the current. Insects abound because they have all been driven to the crowns of the trees and isolated on these islands until the flood recedes.

When the water level drops in the dry season, many lakes that were connected to the river become isolated again for another six to eight months. The local fishermen and the dolphins know that shoals of fish escape from the lakes along narrow streams in order to avoid isolation. So many fish rush down that it is common for them to leap into one's boat. One of the tragedies is that fishermen often net these lake openings and catch everything that tries to escape, including caymans and dolphins. This greedy overfishing is severely reducing the populations of many fish. Sometimes the fish fail to escape into the river and this is where an isolated shoal of piranhas can become dangerous. There is no danger of piranhas attacking humans who swim in the rivers, but in a lake full of starving fish they would attack instantly. Sometimes too many fish are isolated in shallow lakes and the oxygen supply in the water is not enough, so thousands suffocate. One of my most unpleasant experiences in Amazonia was boating through one of these lakes, surrounded by millions of dead, bloated fish. The smell was insupportable but we needed to cross the lake to collect a plant in the forest on the other side!

Raindrops on a banana leaf. Three-quarters of the rain which falls on the forest finds its way back into the air before it has a chance of joining the river system; a quarter of it does not even get as far as the forest floor, evaporating direct from the surfaces of the leaves.

The rivers rise and fall in a regular pattern because of the distribution of rainfall. In Amazonia, there are two seasons: the rainy season, when it rains heavily; and the dry season, when there is much less rain. Rainfall is not uniform throughout the region and the annual precipitation varies from 2 to 3.5 metres. The climate is drier in central Amazonia than in the east near the coast, or in the west near the Andes. It has been shown by the Brazilian climatologist, Eneas Salati, that only 25.9 per cent of the rainfall of central Amazonia runs off into the rivers. Twenty-five point six per cent of the rain evaporates directly from the surface of the vegetation and 48.5 per cent is recycled to the air by the trees through the process of transpiration, by which the trees take in water through their roots and pump it up to the leaves whence it re-enters the atmosphere through the stomata or tiny pores in the leaves.

The fact that only a quarter of the rainfall enters the rivers has severe implications for deforestation. If the forest, which holds so much of the total rainfall, is removed, run-off will increase and extensive flooding will occur. This has already happened to some extent in some deforested areas of Amazonia but in such places as Bangladesh and the Philippines it has been the cause of huge floods. One of the greatest values of the forest is the way in which it controls the circulation of water in the region. Rainfall in eastern Amazonia comes from the Atlantic Ocean and is blown ashore by the prevailing winds. The rain falls on rainforest and therefore 75 per cent is restored to the atmosphere by the process of evapotranspiration. This is then carried further inland and so the process continues towards the west. The consequence of severe deforestation in the east of Amazonia would be a reduction of rainfall in the central region because more of the water would leave by run-off, rather than recycling through the forest. The recently acquired knowledge about the rainfall pattern and the water-holding capacity of the forest is probably the strongest argument against deforestation of the region.

◄ The recycling of water is fundamental to rainforest ecology. Water from the Atlantic is recycled many times through rain, evapotranspiration and cloud.

The natural meeting of ▶ white water and black water can be spectacular, but where the whiteness is the result of destructive mining techniques, the contrast of the silted water seeping into a main tributary can have a sinister overtone. Those responsible are privateer prospectors, *garimpeiros*, who illegally find their way deep into the forest. Unchecked and unmonitored, their activities leave the rivers polluted and the land scarred.

The Amazon River. For part of the year, the river floods. The water level can rise by over 12 metres, inundating the surrounding areas. This flooding is an essential part of the ecology of the region. The weather can change from bright sunshine to a deluge within minutes, and the cloud formations are often both dramatic and beautiful.

The great Amazon River itself is on a scale difficult to comprehend. The v-shape in this photograph is the wake of one of the multitude of river boats which ply this watery trunk road, capable of carrying up to a hundred passengers and their goods. Early adventurers called the Amazon 'Rio-mar' ('River-sea'), and in its lower reaches there are places where neither bank is visible from the centre of the river.

If the rivers are the veins of the Amazon, then the river boats are its blood. They are the only viable collection and distribution system in this huge, inaccessible area. They transport goods to markets in the cities of Belém and Manaus, and carry people slung in forests of hammocks back to their remote homes deep in the green arms of the forest.

▲ A *caboclo* in a canoe. Trade in the Amazon is almost entirely water-borne. Goods for sale are loaded into a canoe and paddled to wherever there may be a market for them, whether it be another *caboclo* settlement half an hour away, or the nearest town three days upstream.

Houses on the Juruá ▶ River. The people who live here are *caboclos*, part-Indian, part-African, with a pinch of Portuguese. They live an isolated life in very small communities, and their only means of communication is the river. Their agricultural practices, which have evolved from the methods of their forest-dwelling ancestors, are sustainable and do little harm to the forest.

THREE

Flowers of the Forest

B ecause of the diversity of species in the forest, there is also a great variety of flower types. Many of the forest trees, such as members of the ubiquitous laurel family, have inconspicuous green flowers which the casual visitor to the forest often passes by, and which may be hard for even the professional botanist to find. To the scientist, however, these are often the most interesting, and for this reason many of the 300 new species of plants I have collected in Amazonia during the last thirty years are of this type. In striking contrast, there are also many spectacular flowers that are showy in some way in order to attract their pollinators. It is this category of flower that also attracts the photographer, and we have some striking examples in this book. The ginger relatives in the order Zingiberales are often photographed because they are large, they grow on the forest floor, and they usually have showy, waxy flowers like the *Heliconia* and *Costus* illustrated here. Most species of this group of plants are bird-pollinated. Birds are attracted by red and pink colours, and humming-birds can frequently be seen hovering in front of a heliconia flower. Heliconia is also one of the favourites of the famous Brazilian artist and landscape designer, Roberto Burle Marx. His tropical gardens often make abundant use of species of heliconia; in fact, one species of heliconia is even named in his honour.

Beaked heliconia (*Heliconia bihai*). The heliconias are most striking tropical flowers pollinated by humming-birds.

Flowers pollinated by bats must be accessible so that the bats can locate them by their sonar navigation system. Since the bats cannot fly into the mass of fine branches of a tree canopy, bat-pollinated flowers either emerge above the crown of the trees or hang below the branches on long stalks. One of the best studied bat-pollinated genus of plants is *Parkia*, whose pompon-like bunch of flowers is always easily accessible, as can be seen in the photograph of *Parkia discolor*. This species has a ring of nectar at the top and a mass of pollen-filled stamens that brush against the bats as they sip the nectar. The kapok or silk cotton tree and the munguba, which both grow beside the rivers of Amazonia, are also bat-pollinated.

Few sights in Amazonia are as spectacular as the simultaneous opening at dusk of the flowers of a lakeful of the royal water lily, *Victoria amazonica*.

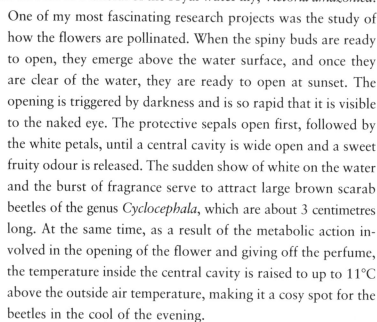

One of my most fascinating research projects was the study of how the flowers are pollinated. When the spiny buds are ready to open, they emerge above the water surface, and once they are clear of the water, they are ready to open at sunset. The opening is triggered by darkness and is so rapid that it is visible to the naked eye. The protective sepals open first, followed by the white petals, until a central cavity is wide open and a sweet fruity odour is released. The sudden show of white on the water and the burst of fragrance serve to attract large brown scarab beetles of the genus *Cyclocephala*, which are about 3 centimetres long. At the same time, as a result of the metabolic action involved in the opening of the flower and giving off the perfume, the temperature inside the central cavity is raised to up to 11°C above the outside air temperature, making it a cosy spot for the beetles in the cool of the evening.

Parkia discolor. Its easily accessible flower is pollinated by bats.

As soon as the flowers open, beetles usually begin to appear and to enter the flowers. Inside the central cavity, there is a circle of knob-like structures called paracarpels; these are full of starch and dextrose, which is just what the beetles like to eat. The beetles begin to eat the paracarpels and are quite content inside the flower. As the night progresses, the central cavity cools, the flowers close up, and the beetles become trapped inside with a supply of food from the paracarpels. An average of eight beetles enter each flower but we once found forty-seven very crushed beetles inside one flower. By dawn, the flower is fully closed, the scent has gone and the temperature has dropped, and one begins to note that the petals are slightly pink.

The flowers stay closed during the day, with the beetles happily munching and resting inside. Meanwhile, the petals continue to change colour, until by mid-afternoon they are a dark reddish-purple, but the inner cavity is still firmly closed. At dusk, when another set of buds on other plants is preparing to open for the first time, the petals and staminodes of the second-night flowers begin to reopen. At this time, the anthers release large quantities of small grains of pollen. The beetles emerge, sticky from the plant juices inside the cavity, and hungry again. As they leave the cavity, they brush against the stamens and become dusted all over with pollen. They take off from the edge of the flower in search of a white, scented, warm, first-night flower. They then repeat the exercise, crawling down into the central cavity, where the pollen rubs off on to the stigmatic surface, thus pollinating the ovaries and allowing the seeds to form. Since plants on a lake produce a flower every second day, the pollen is always carried to a different plant, ensuring cross-pollination. This is a single example of the close coevolution between a plant and its insect pollinator: the beetle depends on the water lily for sustenance and the plant on the beetle for cross-pollination. It is a choreographic relationship as lovely, intricate and formal as a minuet.

The flowers of a vine in the Bignoniaceae or trumpet vine family.

The Amazon Indians have legends about the origins of many of the flowers, trees and crops around them, and one of the loveliest of these is the story of the origin of the royal water lily. Once upon a time there was a chief who had a very beautiful daughter called Naia, whose wedding he was hoping to use to form an alliance with another tribe. She was unhappy about this and used to go down to the lake each evening to contemplate her fate. One night, a beautiful face appeared in the water to comfort her: the reflection of the moon. She fell in love with it, and her love was increased when her father told her that the moon was a great warrior. One evening when she returned to the lake, her lover was gone and she was desperately sad. However, when she returned to the lake two weeks later, there he was again in all his glory. She was so delighted that she plunged into the lake and was drowned. There was great mourning in the tribe. But the fishes in the lake felt sorry for Naia and they asked the moon at least to make her into a star to shine in the sky and to reflect in the water with the moon. The moon heard their cry and turned Naia into a water lily. The Indians went to the lake and found it covered with many white stars, the flowers of the royal water lily, the descendants of Naia.

Such legends serve to produce a respect and reverence for the flowers amongst the Amazon Indians, something that is lacking in westerners, who would cut the forests, pollute the lakes with mercury and spread disease among the Indians. Each flower of the forest could teach us a similar lesson in biology and conservation as the majestic royal water lily.

Monstera deliciosa, a ▶ member of the arum lily family which has become a familiar houseplant and has an edible fruit. Monsteras are pollinated by beetles, using a mechanism similar to that described in the text for the royal water lily.

◀ The royal water lily (*Victoria amazonica*). The leaves are so large and strong that they will support a small child. The flowers change from white to red over a twenty-four-hour period.

◀ (*pp 36–7*) A species of *Calliandra* in the Mimosaceae or mimosa family. The brush-like stamens dust humming-birds with pollen when they visit the flowers.

▲ *Costus* spp. belong to the ginger family (Zingiberaceae). Look for the tiny beetle!

Even fallen leaves can appear geometrically perfect. This is a leaf of *Bauhinia*; its divided form gives rise to its local name, *unha de gado*, meaning cow's hoof.

Caladium bicolor in the arum lily family, one of the many Amazonian species to find its way into the living rooms of homes in temperate climates as a houseplant. Its ability to grow in the low light intensity of the rainforest helps it to survive in similar conditions indoors.

FOUR

Fruits of the Forest

The Amazonian Indians have adapted well to the phenomenal species diversity of their forests. They have found uses for a large percentage of the plant species that surround them. Recent studies in quantitative ethnobotany carried out by botanists and anthropologists of the New York Botanical Garden Institute of Economic Botany show the extent to which the Indians use the rainforest trees. Inventories were made of all the trees over 10 centimetres diameter in one-hectare plots of forest, and then a record was made of which species the Indians use in any way. A study by botanist Brian

Pupunha (*Bactris gasipaes*), a favourite breakfast dish when boiled and eaten with sweet coffee. This attractive and colourful fruit is widely available in markets throughout the region and is grown by most Indian tribes.

Boom with the Chácobo Indians of Bolivia showed that in his sample hectare the Indians had uses for seventy-six of the ninety-four species (78.7 per cent). There were 649 trees of 10 centimetres diameter or more, of which 616 were usable, i.e. 95 per cent. Another study by anthropologist William Balée, showed that the Ka'apor Indians used seventy-six out of ninety-nine species on his sample plot, and the Tembe Indians seventy-three out of 119 species (61.3 per cent). These and other similar studies indicate that the forests are full of useful species of plants, which provide food, building material, fibres, medicines, dyes and a host of other items.

A visit to any market in an Amazonian city, town or village will show that there is a great variety of fruit available. Some would be familiar, such as bananas and oranges, neither of which are Amazonian natives, but others would be less familiar in our markets but equally useful to the Amazon residents. One of the fruits most frequently found are the large pods of the cacau tree, which produces the chocolate bean. In Amazonia, the residents eat the delicious pulp that surrounds the seeds or beans. The cacau is a common tree, particularly in flooded forests beside the rivers. It has long been used by Amazonian natives, and its use had already spread throughout the neotropics in pre-Columbian times. Here we have photographs of two other species of the cacau genus *Theobroma* (or food of the gods). Of all Amazon fruits, my favourite is *Theobroma grandiflorum*, known as the cupuaçú. It is well named because *cupu* is the Tupi for cacau and *açú* means large. The brown, furry, oblong fruits can be as large as a rugby football. The pulp around the seeds makes the most delicious aromatic dessert or ice-cream. It is one of the fruits for which I am trying to develop a market in the United Kingdom in order to increase the number of products harvested from the forest. The second species illustrated here is *Theobroma bicolor*, which has a ridged fruit and is known locally in Amazonian Peru as macambo. It is the disc-like seeds of macambo that are eaten. They are roasted on a spit and make a delicious nutty canapé.

Cashew fruit and nut (*Anacardium occidentale*). A striking fruit with the nut unexpectedly protruding from the fleshy pear, which is really a swollen stem and not a fruit at all.

The cashew pear is an unusual fruit that is technically a swollen stem, rather than a fruit. The comma-shaped nut, which is the true fruit, is borne at the apex of a fleshy, pear-shaped structure. The pear is red or yellow, juicy and sweet but slightly astringent to human taste. It is a favourite for fruit drinks and is rich in vitamins. The nut, on the other hand, is quite poisonous, unless roasted. The reason for this structure and, indeed, that of many fruits, is to aid the dispersal of the seeds from one place to another. Birds are fond of the appetising pear and like to carry it off to eat. They do not touch the poisonous nut and so it is rejected and in the process dispersed around the forest. The cashew of commerce is a low tree of the drier fringes of the Amazon forest, but there are other species of the cashew genus (*Anacardium*), which are amongst the tallest in the forest, as is evident from the name of one species, *Anacardium giganteum*.

The calabash is the gourd of the Amazon. It is a large round fruit, about the size of a football, which is borne on the trunk and mature branches of the trees. After a bat has pollinated the green tubular flower, the young fruit begins to develop. As it appears, it is covered with small pale studs which secrete nectar. Fierce ants soon begin to feast on the nectar and drive away any other animal that tries to eat the young fruit. As the fruit swells up and becomes hard and woody, there is no longer any need for it to be protected by the ants and the nectaries dry up and become inconspicuous. Without the action of a bat and the ants, the Amazon residents would not have many of these most useful fruits, which they turn into water pots, soup bowls, canoe balers and many other domestic items.

Guaraná is one of the most popular Amazonian beverages today. This caffeine-rich soda drink, made from the seed of the guaraná plant (*Paullinia cupana*), is the coca-cola of Brazil. Long before it was turned into an item of commerce, the Maué Indians used to roast the seeds, grind them into a powder and mix the powder with water to make a drink before setting off for a day's hunting or work in the fields. With the stimulation of these seeds, they were not hungry and had enough energy to last through the day without food.

The black seed of guaraná is surrounded by a white pulp called the aril, which in turn is enclosed by a bright red outer shell. When this shell opens, the fruit has an eye-like appearance, which obviously gave rise to the Indian legend for guaraná. However, this attractive and conspicuous fruit evolved to capture the attention of birds, which eat the pulp and reject the seed but in the process disperse it round the forest.

Maué legend tells of a time when the tribe was going through many tribulations. They had lost much of their land in wars with neighbouring tribes. A wonder child was born to an elderly childless couple. The boy became the tribe's leader and helped them to defeat their enemies and to prosper. The evil gods were jealous of the good fortune of the Maué people and plotted to destroy this remarkable boy. One of the evil spirits, Jurupari, turned himself into a poisonous snake. The gods also caused a fruit tree to bear delicious fruits, and the snake waited in its branches. Eventually the boy hero climbed the tree, was bitten by the snake and fell down dead. There was great mourning throughout the tribe and their fortunes began to decline. However, Tupa, the good god, sent lightning to strike the child's mother but, before she died, he told her not to despair as great good would come out of this apparent disaster. The mother was instructed to take the eyes of the child and plant them in a field. Out of the left eye came a new plant they had not seen before which they called guaraná, or the living eye, and out of the right eye, wild guaraná. The strength given by guaraná maintained their tribal superiority. The fact that the legend includes the wild guaraná, the many wild species of *Paullinia*, is significant. To maintain many crop plants the genetic material of the wild species is essential for properties such as disease resistance. It is essential to conserve the wild relatives of crop plants. The guaraná legend draws attention to and adds to the Indians' respect for the wild species.

The calabash (*Crescentia cujete*) provides containers in a multitude of sizes, big enough to hold soup to feed a family, or small enough to be used as a spoon to eat it.

Details about the fruits of Amazonia could fill a lengthy volume. The delicious guava, the anonas or soursops, and even the papaya or pawpaw, all originated in the Amazon region, but I have room to speak of just one more fruit with which I have a love/hate relationship. On one of my expeditions, the light aircraft which we were using crashed on landing at the jungle airstrip of Uaicá in the north of Roraima State, near the Venezuelan frontier with Brazil. Our party of eight people was left without food because we flew in people on the first of two planned flights and expected to bring in the supplies on the second one. We were left to live off the fruits of the forest! With both a botanist and an experienced woodsman on the expedition, we did not starve because there was a grove of peach palm or pupunha trees (*Bactris gasipaes*) near the airstrip. We soon devised an apparatus on the end of a long pole to harvest the fruits from the top of the extremely spinous trunk. For the first two days we ate peach palms for breakfast, lunch and dinner. By the third day, we noticed a reduction in our daily consumption of these fruit. By the end of a week, when offered a peach palm for breakfast, I noticed that most of us refused. However, this nutritious fruit, which tastes rather like chestnut, served as our staple for ten days until we were rescued. It was a very long time before I could face another pupunha fruit. This does not do justice to what is in fact one of the most popular fruits of the region. Before the crash, we frequently boiled them and served them with mayonnaise as an appetiser.

The useful plant products of Amazonia are legion. The peoples of the region depend upon two in particular for their livelihood. These are rubber and Brazil nuts, derived from two of the best known and most commercialised native species. Wild rubber trees are tapped during the dry season and Brazil nuts are gathered during the rainy season, thus giving the local residents work all the year round. In recent years, the rubber tappers have frequently come into conflict with developers who seek to fell the forests upon which the tappers depend. The best known rubber tapper was Francisco (Chico) Mendes, leader of the tappers' union of the State of Acre. He was gunned down in December 1988 for his resistance to deforestation. This death, and that of many fellow rubber tappers, eventually led to the establishment of a number of extractive reserves in Acre and other states, where the tappers are free to live and extract products from the forest but not to cut it down. A challenge to industry and science today is to develop new products other than timber that can be extracted from the forest without felling and that will have a reasonable market price in the developed world. The future stability of extractive reserves and the conservation of the species of plants and animals which they contain will depend upon the development of a diversity of new commercial products in addition to rubber and Brazil nuts. The studies in quantitative ethnobotany of the Indians described at the beginning of this chapter show the potential that lies in the biological diversity of the forest. The cupuaçú fruit must be just one of many new extraction crops to be discovered from the Amazon forests, and today many people are working both to develop the use of the fruits of the forest and to conserve them. This type of co-operation between forest peoples, scientists, technicians and enlightened industries in identifying and developing new products is one of the signs of hope for a viable future for Amazonia and its people.

◀ Cupuaçú (*Theobroma grandiflorum*), the best-kept secret of the Amazon. This fruit, probably more than any other, has a huge potential market elsewhere in the world as a flavouring for desserts and ice-creams.

A Brazil nut tree (*Berthol-* ▶ *letia excelsa*). The nuts which enrich the European Christmas grow inside an *ouriço*, a very hard shell the size of a large grapefruit, which contains about a dozen or more nuts. The trees grow to a height of 40 metres. The Kayapó Indians now derive an important income from collecting and pressing the nuts. The oil is sold direct to the Body Shop and is used in products from their Rainforest range of toiletries.

◀ Mamão (*Carica papaya*). Better known as papaya, the Brazilian version is often the size of a rugby football. The fruits ripen one by one over an extended season, giving the tree's owner a continuous supply. The seeds have several medicinal uses; they are used to treat intestinal parasites and as an abortifacient.

▲ Guaraná (*Paullinia cupana*). Although used to flavour Brazil's most popular soft drink, guaraná is only now becoming a little more widely known. Brazilian Indians form the berries into hard sticks by roasting and mixing with cassava gum. The stick is grated using the dried tongue of a fish, and the powder thus produced is mixed with water, to make an effective tonic.

▲ Young fruit of macambo (*Theobroma bicolor*). When mature, it is up to 30 centimetres long. This relative of the cacao or chocolate plant is popular with the Indians of the upper Amazon, who roast the seeds on a spit to make a tasty snack.

Guava (*Psidium guajava*). ▶ The fruit can be eaten fresh, or made into a sweet and sticky gelatinous confection with some similarity to Turkish Delight (but much richer). The leaves may be made into a tea for the treatment of stomach complaints.

FIVE

The People of the Forest

The beautiful photographs of the Indians in this book show that there are still a few relatively undisturbed tribes living in much the same way that they did before the arrival of the conquistadors from Europe. However, what we see today is a mere vestige of the former population. As archaeological studies progress, the estimated size of the pre-Columbian population of Amazonia increases. It is now thought that there were over 5 million inhabitants in lowland Amazonia. Some tribes were huge; for example, the Omagua who lived along the reaches of the upper Amazon.

Most Brazilian Indians love the water, and spend a huge amount of time washing themselves and swimming. It is an opportunity for adults and children to share. Here, Bengotí gives his nephew a cuddle. The boy's name is Gordon, after Gordon Roddick, the Body Shop chairman.

However, persecution, warfare and the introduction of western diseases to which they had no resistance had reduced the Amazonian population to 1 million by 1900. Brazilian anthropologist Darcy Ribeiro estimated that there were 230 tribal groups in 1900 but that by 1957 there were only 143 remaining. Eighty-seven entire tribes and all the cultural information they contained were destroyed in a fifty-seven-year period. Tribal extinction has continued throughout the last three decades as highways have been opened up, large cattle ranches have been created, and land-hungry colonists have deforested the State of Rondônia. There is no doubt that at least one tribe has become extinct for every year of the twentieth century, and today's estimates of the Indian population are between 100,000 and 150,000. This makes more precious the culture of the remaining peoples, such as the Yanomami and the Kayapó, who know how to manage and survive in the Amazon rainforest.

Most westerners who have spent any length of time amongst the Indians, whether as photographers, ethnobotanists or anthropologists, have soon come to respect their culture and to realise their amazing adaptation to life in the rainforest. While not all is harmonious, and most of us would not go as far as Rousseau's concept of the noble savage, we do have a lot to learn from the Indian experience of several millennia of living in the Amazon rainforest. Many of their taboos, beliefs and practices protect the forest rather than destroy it. There was plenty of game and no danger of extinction of manatees, river turtles, crocodiles or brightly coloured parrots before western man conquered the region. Today, scientists are studying the Indian land-use pattern and their ecology to gain information about how to use the land in sustainable ways.

Indian agriculture is based on diversity of species and varieties, rather than monocultures of genetically uniform crops. Over the years, they have developed an agroforestry system of intercropping that gives a mixture of trees, shrubs and herbs and uses the process of natural regeneration of the forest in a controlled way. The Indian system clears a relatively small area of land that is surrounded by forest, so that the seeds of the trees are ready to recolonise the felled areas. Recent studies of charcoal deposits in the soil, using the process of radio-carbon dating, show that a surprisingly large amount of the apparently virgin rainforest has been cleared at one time or another. The difference between this and today's deforestation for cattle pasture is that the Indians' clearance was carried out in small patches and that what they used to replace the forest was an agricultural system that was much more compatible with the poor soils of the region.

The islands of forest that are found in the savannahs near Kayapó villages are a good illustration of indigenous methods of agriculture and forest management. Ethnobiologists studying the Kayapó Indians noted a greater frequency of these forest islands in the savannahs near villages than further afield. This led to the

Indigenous technology relies on forest products. Kubeni-caití, a Kayapó elder, forms a hole in a piece of wood to make a pipe, using a harder wood with a resin-based abrasive as a drill.

discovery that many of the islands were in fact man-made. These *apêtês*, as they are called by the Kayapó, start as compost heaps in the nearby forest. At the beginning of the rainy season, the resulting mulch is taken to a depression in the savannah that is likely to hold water during the rains. The mulch is then mixed with soil from termite mounds and ants' nests, together with living ants. A mound of earth about 2 metres in diameter is formed and planted with useful trees. Over the years, the Indians continue to plant around the edge of the island until a large patch of forest is formed that contains all the necessities of life: food, medicines, fibres and other products. Some fruit trees are even planted for the express purpose of attracting game. Formerly, the *apêtês* were useful refuges in time of tribal warfare; today they are a useful supermarket. The study of the way in which the Kayapó turn savannah into a productive forest is most informative for learning about methods of reforestation. The Indians are able to create and manage a most productive forest. Amongst their management techniques for *apêtês* is the way the Kayapó make use of the pungent *Azteca* ant to repel leaf-cutter ants, one of the worst pests of cultivated fields in Amazonia. The Indians break off small pieces of the strong-smelling *Azteca* ant colonies and carry them to each forest patch where no colony exists. They have been using biological control long before it became a useful tool in our society.

The staple food of the Amazon is the manioc or mandioca root (*Manihot esculenta*), which is cultivated by most tribes of Indians, the *caboclos* and other settlers, and has been introduced around the tropics as an important source of carbohydrate and tapioca. One wonders how its use was first discovered, because the fresh root is full of cyanide poisons. Some of Gonzalo Pizarro's men in search of El Dorado in 1538 died when they ate unprocessed manioc roots which they found in an Indian canoe. The root must be soaked, grated, squeezed or pressed to remove the poisonous juices, and then roasted to remove the last of the toxic substances. The Indians have devised various apparatuses to process the mandioca. The juices are squeezed out, either in a press or in a basketwork hanging strainer called a *tipiti*. This is like an enlarged Chinese finger puller that contracts when a stick is put through a loop at the base, fixed at one end and then sat on at the other to use it as a lever to weigh down the strainer. The juice runs out and the residue is then toasted on a large flat plate. The Indians used a ceramic plate on top of a mud-walled oven with the fire underneath. Early settlers soon introduced copper plates and today these plates are made of steel. The end product is a gritty flour called *farinha* that the Indians mix with their food.

A legend of the Mundurucu Indians tells of an old man who lived with his daughter beside a small stream. His daughter Ruda was very beautiful and had taken good care of her father since her mother died. They lived alone, far from the rest of the tribe, because the man was afraid that his daughter might become pregnant. One day, the father noticed that Ruda was very sad, and he was furious when he discovered that his worst fear had come true: Ruda was pregnant. In his rage he wished to kill her because it was so shameful. As he was planning how to kill his daughter, a white man came along and persuaded him to let Ruda have her baby because it was the dolphin that had made her pregnant. The white man was the god Tupa in disguise. The Indian belief or excuse for an unexplainable pregnancy which blames the dolphin has passed into rural Amazonian society. *Caboclos* often tell how the dolphin dons a top hat to cover his blow-hole, disguises himself as a human and appears at a party and seduces the young girls. Many Amazonian parents still blame the dolphin for children which are born out of wedlock.

Several months later, a lovely baby girl was born and Ruda called her Mani. She was talking from the day she was born and was helping her mother with the work by the time she was six months old. She brought great joy to the Mundurucus and the whole tribe would bring her presents. However, Mani was a spirit child and did not belong on earth, and after a year she died and returned to the sky.

The birds stopped singing, the water lily flowers withered, and there was great mourning. Ruda buried Mani in front of her house and planted a beautiful garden around her. However, a strange plant came up in the middle which the Mundurucu had never seen before. It had a large white root, just like Mani's body, and so the Indians called it 'Manioca' or house of Mani's body. Many Amazonians still believe today that if a child is very precocious or learns to speak too soon, it will die young.

The Indians obtain all the necessities of life from the forest, and plant products are crucial, not just for food and medicines, but also as sources of cooking and lighting oil, arrow and fish poisons, and to supply bark and fibres for clothing, ropes and baskets. The variety of Amazonian plant species used by the Indians is so enormous because different tribes use different plants for the same applications, for example, the many species which are used throughout Amazonia as fish poisons.

Fish poisons are a particularly important plant product for the Amazonian peoples. The method used is to place plant juices containing the poison, known as *timbo*, in a small stream. Fish caught this way are quite safe to eat, as most of the chemicals used break down the gill membranes of the fish and suffocate them, rather than poison them, strictly speaking. Every tribe of Indians that I have visited has a fish poison of some kind. Many different plants are used, but the poisons are most commonly derived from the *Lonchocarpus* vine, a member of the legume family.

Irepá, a Kayapó woman elder from the Xingu park. Irepá has become a good friend and spiritual guide to Sue.

The Maku of the upper Rio Negro region of Brazil and Colombia are especially well known for their fishing feasts, and I collected eight different fish poisons from this tribe alone. When it is time for a fishing feast, the whole tribe goes off into the forest to find a suitable stream. This can take some time. When I accompanied people from a Maku village on one such expedition, we walked for eight hours and crossed three or four streams of the appropriate size until we reached the water they wanted to fish. When asked why we did not stop earlier, the chief told me that it was the turn of this stream because the others had been fished more recently and, if they fished too often, there would be no fish left. How different from our attitude to the herring and cod in the North Sea! The people had been carrying huge panniers of *timbo* leaves on their backs, on this occasion leaves of the spurge *Euphorbia cotinifolia*. They built a log bridge over the stream and placed their baskets on it. Some of the women went upstream of the bridge and stirred up the stream bottom to make the water muddy; the men proceeded to beat the leaves so that the plant juices dripped down into the water. The rest of the group, including quite small children, had a great time splashing about in the water collecting the fish into freshly woven baskets of palm leaf. The bounty was great, including the smallest of fish, which were quickly roasted over a fire beside the stream. I rapidly had my fill, but the Indians ate enormous quantities during this time of plenty.

Fishing expeditions using poisons are communal activities. These trips often take the Indians far from their villages to fish the rivers in rotation, thus maintaining the natural balance. If a family requires fish just for themselves, however, they will net or spear a fish or two close to the village.

One of the most important tasks in order to increase our knowledge of the rainforest and how to manage it wisely is the study of the indigenous ethnobiology. There is a need for much more documentation by anthropologists, botanists, photographers and agroforesters of the Indians' way of life. However, in the process of learning, I hope that we can help these people to maintain their dignity and integrity, rather than just use them as a way to learn about the forest and then usurp their territories, as has happened in the past. There are signs, as we shall see in the last section of this book, that things are improving and the Indians are gaining more respect and protection.

◄ There are huge differences between the Indian groups in Brazil, which are reflected in the way their villages are laid out. The Kayapó build their houses in a circle, with the *nobe*, or men's hut, at the centre (bottom left). The *nobe* is the seat of local government. Here the village discusses its problems and reaches its decisions, in a way which could teach many westerners a great deal about democracy! When the roof needs to be replaced, the whole community lends a hand (top left).

▲ The Yanomami build a single, large *yano*, which typically houses a community of about eighty. Inside, each family group has a fire, around which they hang their hammocks. The *yano* is dark, but lofty and imposing.

▲ The Indians are not the only people living in the forest in a non-destructive way. A century ago, during the rubber boom, thousands of people of mixed Indian-African-European ancestry were encouraged to move from the poor north-east of Brazil into the forests, to collect the precious latex. The descendants of these *seringueiros* still live in the forest, although their livelihood is under threat from falling rubber prices and the destruction of the forests.

The Yanomami use ▶ unusually long arrows, which they shoot with unerring accuracy and power. They learn this skill at a very early age.

▲ Many indigenous communities still retain most of their cultural and craft traditions, despite awareness of industrial products. Here, a Metuktire-Kayapó man from the Xingu Indian Park weaves a basket; he and some of the other men in his village still sport a *botoque*, the traditional lip plate. The art of basket-weaving is highly developed. There are as many types and designs of basketwork as there are uses. In the picture above right, pineapples (*Ananas comosus*) are carried in a basket slung about the carrier's forehead.

The Indians eat many ▶ seasonal foods, and the ripening of a particular fruit can be the signal for the women to go on a collecting party. Açaí (*Euterpe* sp.) is a highly valued palm fruit which forms a deep purple pulp with a strong flavour. It is rich in vitamins and trace elements, and is an important dietary supplement.

Manioc (*Manihot esculenta*) (opposite, top left) is the most important staple food for all rural Amazon people. The Indians use a number of distinct varieties, one of which is capable of surviving great heat. It is planted after the forest has been cleared on a new cultivation site, but before it has been burnt. The root is thus able to take up the nutrients released by the burning before they can be leached out.

The first process in the preparation of manioc flour is to peel and grate the root, making a wet, spongy dough (opposite, top right). It is then squeezed in a strainer made of open-weave palm leaves; this removes most of the toxins present. The manioc now has a crumbly texture (bottom). Finally, it is roasted in a large steel bowl (above). Historically, Indians used a flat earthenware plate for this stage, but this is now rare.

▲ Another important food is the Brazil nut, which is also collected for trading. Indians, rubber tappers and *caboclos* sell the nuts to itinerant traders who travel along the rivers, paying very little for the nuts and selling the few manufactured goods the forest people use at inflated prices. The nut collectors in this photograph are Kayapó Indians.

Displaced, disorientated ▶ and disillusioned, a Yanomami mother waits with her children beside an airstrip illegally carved out of the forest by gold-hungry *garimpeiros*. Her future is bleak; it is estimated that as many as 20 per cent of the Yanomami have died in the last three years because of the miners. They die of disease, malnutrition and poisoning of their water supply and food chain.

◀ A woman from a Xicrin-Kayapó village spins cotton thread. Threads made in this way are used to make hammocks, and to hold the feathers together in the glorious headdresses worn by the men.

▲ A young member of a very old people. But will her people still exist when she is fully grown?

SIX

Adornment

A dornment is a vital part of tribal ritual, and the decorations used are often vivid and showy, as can be seen in the photographs. Some tribes pierce their ears, and some distort their lower lips with a large disc of wood. The Yanomami often wear feathers or leaves in their ears and a series of thin sticks in holes round their mouths. Each tribe has a slightly different style of decoration, and the patterns often have special meaning for the individuals involved.

One of the most striking forms of adornment is body painting. The substances used derive from many different plants, but two are universal and are certainly the most important. Most bright red or scarlet body paint comes from the urucum plant, *Bixa orellana* or *achiote*, as it is called in the Spanish-speaking countries. The urucum is a low, shrubby plant and the dye comes from the aril that surrounds the seeds. The seeds are produced in bright red, hairy capsules which decorate the bush like Christmas-tree ornaments. Every Indian garden is brightened by a group of *achiote* plants. The colouring can be applied directly by simply rubbing the seeds on to the body, but if a large quantity is needed, a mass of seeds is boiled in a pan to produce a sticky paste. It has been found that body paint from urucum repels insects, so the use of this material has a secondary benefit. In Brazil, urucum has been used for many years as a food colourant, and boiled rice is usually coloured pink with a powdered form called *colorão*; it is also marketed internationally as the spice annatto. More recently, with the discovery of the toxic effects of various red food dyes, the dye derived from urucum has become an important colouring agent in the modern food industry: yet another useful product that came to us from the Amazon Indians.

This man, Ta'Kiré, is wearing the blue feathers of a macaw, red urucum paint, and a necklace of shells, the sign of a warrior.

The Kayapó Indian women often mix the crushed bodies of a little red ant, the *mrum-re* ant, in with their red body paint. This ant is the guardian of the fields, and is our relative, say the women. Unlike the fire ant, which is aggressive and resembles men, the little red ant is gentle, they say, as women are. It is the women who cultivate the fields in this society, and they are the ones who know about the ants' behaviour. Manioc, the staple root crop, produces nectar on the vegetative parts of the young plants, and this attracts the *mrum-re* ants, who protect the manioc by driving off other leaf-eating insects and by cutting off any vines that grow on to the plant. The use of the ants in the women's body paint has obviously come from this realisation of the ecological role of the ant and has been turned into a suitable myth.

The most used black dye is made from the fruits of the genipapo tree (*Genipa americana*). The photographs show how shiny and effective this dye is. This is because it undergoes a subcutaneous reaction with the skin and is thus semi-permanent. It is not possible to wash off much of this dye, a fact which my daughter discovered to her cost when she was elaborately painted on her cheeks by the Bora Indians of Peru. There were still faint traces of the patterns by the time our ship reached Rio de Janeiro three weeks later! In some tribes, when a child is sick, they will dye the entire body with genipapo as part of the treatment.

The black is used as a background dye, but the Indians prefer the colours red and blue. On my first expedition to the Yanomami, I took glass beads of many different colours as trading gifts for the Indians. The red and blue beads were by far the most popular, and they completely rejected the green and yellow beads which I had to offer. The only other colour they would take was white. I soon learned to take only the preferred colours on future expeditions. I suppose that if you live in a forest surrounded by such an array of shades of green, you do not want artificially coloured green beads.

In their use of beads, the Indians are by no means confined to the glass ones obtained by trading. Their necklaces may contain animal bones, teeth, fish scales and wood carvings, as well as natural beads chosen from the wonderful diversity of seeds available in the forest. So many different seeds are used throughout the Amazon that one could write a whole book on that topic alone. However, perhaps the most used natural beads are the seeds of the tento (*Ormosia*) tree, a member of the bean family. The fruit of this plant is pseudo-arillate; that is, it looks as if it has a fleshy aril. The seeds are red, with a black base, and superficially resemble guaraná seeds. They are dispersed by birds, who are deceived by the colours and shape into thinking that they offer a juicy reward. They are very hard, and so long as they are kept dry, they will last for years, making them an ideal red bead.

Another popular bead, the Job's tear, originated in tropical Asia, but must have been introduced into Amazonia at an early stage because it is worn by even some of the remotest tribes. This shiny grey bead is produced by a member of the grass family, *Coix lacryma-jobi*, which has what is, for a grass, a most unusual hard seed that makes a perfect bead.

Adornment amongst the Amazonian peoples is not a sign of vanity and boasting. Although they are often proud of their appearance when well painted, the patterns they use are deeply symbolic and represent an important part of their cultural life. Body paint tells us about their history, their relationships and their achievements.

Urucum (*Bixa orellana*), or annatto. A vital component of Indian adornment is the bright red dye derived from these spiny red pods and the seeds they contain. It is used for everything, from an insect-repelling dye applied to the ankle, to a thick goo caked on to the hair.

To an outsider's view, the sticks protruding from the face of a Yanomami can be disturbing, but within the tribe they are an essential part of a girl's attire. The ear lobes often have quite large holes, which are decorated with feathers, flowers or leaves. Yanomami body painting is often less geometric than that of the Kayapó, leaving the skin looking flecked.

(*pp 78–9*) Black dye ▶ based on the pulp of the genipapo fruit is applied with the deft use of a thin stick. The act of painting a child's face (left) is very loving, and helps to create the strong bond between a mother and her child. The designs of face paint can be incredibly intricate. The dye can last several weeks; the pattern on the baby's face (right) is barely discernible, while his mother's has only just been applied.

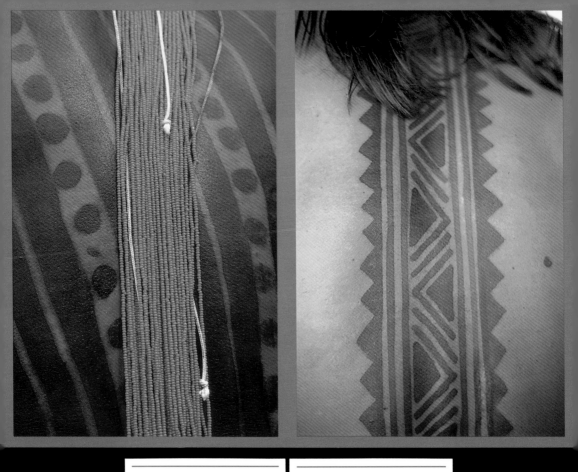

▲ There is wide variety in styles of body painting within a particular tribe. The patterns used in the black skin dye reflect the character of the individual. The two shown on this page come from the same Kayapó village. Indians also have plenty of scope for expressing individuality in their other adornments; imported bright blue and red beads are common, as are brightly coloured feathers of all sizes, but virtually everything found in the forest – seeds, flowers, leaves, stones, wood – is used by someone.

The Yanomami style of ▶ adornment is markedly different from that of the Kayapó. The colours used are often yellows and blacks, and the arrangements tend to be somewhat less formal. Very small downy feathers are used extensively.

SEVEN

The Healing Forest

One of the arguments most frequently used to defend the rainforest against destruction is the fact that it contains so many undiscovered medicines of great potential for the future. This is certainly true because less than 5 per cent of the plant species of Amazonia have been tested medicinally and they contain a great array of toxic chemicals as a defence against the hordes of plant-eating insects that live in the forest. Some important drugs which have already come from the region include quinine, ipecac, curare and pilocarpine. All these entered Western usage because they were previously used in some way by indigenous peoples. Most Indian tribes have a large pharmacopoeia of plant-derived medicines. The use of many of these has spread to the entire Amazon population, and the markets of cities such as Belém, Santarém, Manaus and Iquitos have fascinating medicinal plant sections. One can buy a cure for almost anything, together with details of how to prepare the brew or apply the paste. Ethnobotanist Elizabeth van den Berg identified 1200 medicinal plants on sale in the Ver-o-peso market of Belém. It is an enlightening experience to go to the market, pretend to have a pain somewhere and ask for a cure. When I have done this, I have been impressed by the consistency of the cure from one market stall to another.

The appearance of a plant may often suggest its medicinal use, and in this the Amazon Indians resemble the herbalists of medieval Europe, with their doctrine of signatures; for example, the snake-like rhizomes of some species of the fern *Polypodium* are frequently used as a remedy for snake bites. The most frequently used aphrodisiac is made from

Herbal medicines on sale in a market. Brazil's poor have traditionally relied heavily on herbal remedies, which are often extremely effective in the treatment of common disorders. Advertising by pharmaceutical companies in the last few decades has substantially eroded this, with the result that the poor spend a high proportion of their income on manufactured medicines. These are often incorrectly dispensed by untrained people.

83

the roots of species of *Psychotria* (*Cephaelis*) that have two large, scarlet, lip-like bracts surrounding the flowers. It has the appearance of luscious lips and so its use as an aphrodisiac is not surprising. It is interesting that ipecac comes from a closely related species of *Psychotria*. The familiar garden plant *Celosia cristata* is also grown by many Indian tribes and by the *caboclos*. Medicinally, it is used as a tea to stop haemorrhages; a plant with bright red flowers has become the remedy for stemming the flow of blood. One can see the obvious application of the doctrine of signatures in many Amazon medicines.

Another way in which medicines have been discovered is through the use of hallucinogens by shamans. The shamans of the upper Amazon are famous for their use of the hallucinogenic beverage *ayuhuasca*, derived from the vine *Banisteriopsis caapi* mixed together with the leaves of *Psychotria viridis*. The trance state helps the shaman to discover which plant to use for the treatment of a particular ailment, and many new medicinal plants have entered their lives this way.

For cuts and bruises, I have frequently used the Indian remedy of andiroba oil, which is extracted from the seeds of the mahogany relative, *Carapa guianensis*. This oil is much used by the Indians, both medicinally and to oil their bodies. It also acts as an insect repellent and so it is hardly surprising that they like to use it liberally! The Indians have discovered a number of ways to repel insects, whether on their bodies or in their fields. One of the plants most used for this purpose is lemon grass, *Cymbopogon citratus*, which has a strong lemon fragrance. It can be rubbed on to the body to repel insects, but it is also planted amongst herbaceous crops for the same reason: another example of the Indians' use of biological control of pests in their fields.

Lemon grass (*Cymbopogon citratus*). The oily extract is rubbed on the skin as an insect repellent. This plant also provides the ingredients for conventional medicines, and the leaves are used for a tasty tea.

One of the tasks of the ethnobotanist studying herbal medicines is to distinguish magic plants from medicines. Early in my career, I remember a

Mayongong Indian from Auaris in Roraima State telling me all about a fantastic medicinal plant that would remove all back pains. I duly noted down the details and made a collection of the plant, a species of *Pithecellobium*, with fine, delicate, fern-like leaflets. Fortunately, I asked how he used it. The Indian made one of my team bend over, waved the branch about in the air furiously and then brushed it gently over his back. He screeched and screamed a chant and then assured us that José would have no more back problems. This plant would be an unlikely candidate for chemical analysis if one were looking for new medicines. If, on the other hand, an Indian boiled up a tea of bark or leaves and drank it, it would be much more likely to contain an active chemical compound. I have often had stomach upsets and diarrhoea cured by a tea brewed by the Indians.

Today, many people are using ethnobotanical information as a way to discover new medicines. It is important to ensure that the indigenous people who provide the information benefit from any such discoveries. All too often their ideas have been taken and they have reaped no reward from major commercialisation of their knowledge. The ethnobotanists, pharmacologists and chemists of the future must ensure that the intellectual property rights of indigenous people are respected.

Crista de Gallo (*Celosia cristata*). The large, vibrant, blood-red flowers give a guide to the use of the plant: it is made into a tea to treat internal haemorrhages.

◄ *Brugmansia insignis*. The regal, lantern-shaped flowers with their delicate nuances of colour are magnificently imposing. The plant, and especially the seeds, are rich in clinically active agents, and it is the subject of on-going research to establish the mechanisms of its toxicity.

▲ Açacaca (*Croton caju-cara*). There has been promising research into the use of this plant as the basis for a slimming aid. It also contains the same essential oil – linalol – as that found in Brazilian rosewood, which has been much felled to extract it. The use of açacaca, a common shrub of secondary forest, as a source of linalol could help to end the over-exploitation of rosewood.

Psychotria poeppigiana. The generous lips of the flower are the clue to the use of its roots as an aphrodisiac, a superb example of the doctrine of signatures.

Andiroba (*Carapa guianensis*). The seeds of this tree contain an excellent oil for the skin and for treating superficial cuts, bruises and abrasions. The Body Shop researched andiroba oil for cosmetic use, but it was found to contain a high proportion of clinically active components which rendered it unsuitable for use in their products.

Imbaúba (*Cecropia* sp.), a common tree of disturbed areas, which grows in light gaps where other trees have fallen. The leaves are used as a tea for the treatment of stomach upsets.

Jatobá (*Hymenaea courbar-il*). Many Amazonian herbal medicines are extracted from tree species. The Indian and *caboclo* people usually do this in a non-destructive way. For example, only a little bark is taken from each tree, or the resin is bled in a way which does not kill the tree. Unfortunately, when a particular remedy becomes known to opportunists from the city, the relevant species can suffer large-scale destruction for their short-term gain.

EIGHT

Environmental Destruction

When I first went to the rainforests of Suriname in 1963, I was happy just to be a botanist studying the flora, the biology and the way in which the local people used plants. I continued this basic research work on an inventory of Amazonian plants for the next decade, mainly in the Brazilian Amazon. However, in 1973, when I was living in Manaus and working to set up a graduate programme in botany and ecology, my vision of the needs of Amazonia was dramatically changed by a class field trip to study the impact of the newly inaugurated Trans-Amazon highway. We took the students to what was then the small town of Altamira in Pará State. The class was being taught by Robert Goodland, an environmental impact ecologist who is now working for the World Bank. What we saw appalled us. The highway was built after President Medici visited northeast Brazil at a time of drought and saw the massive starvation there. His solution was to build a road across the Amazon basin, accompanied by a series of villages, towns and cities to accommodate millions of hungry north-easterners. Thus good humanitarian reasons, together with the desire of the military government of that time to open up the Amazon, led to this new road.

As roads are thrust through the forest at breakneck speed, it is common for small valleys to be crossed by simply constructing an embankment across them, instead of building a bridge. This acts as a dam to any stream draining the valley, which quickly fills with water, drowning the trees. The resulting landscape of stark, dead, white tree trunks is an eerie reminder of the destructive force of man.

We visited settlers, villages called *agrovilas*, and towns called *agropolises*, and even stayed in the beginnings of one of the cities, called Ruropolis Presidente Medici. It was obvious, even at that early stage, that many of the settlers were bitterly disappointed by their Amazonian experience. Their farming, according to the agricultural extension advice they had been given by the government, was to be based on upland rice. The first year's harvest failed because of dry weather and they were unable to pay their mortgages on the houses provided by the government. The area in Pará through which the highway passes is also on some of the poorest soil in the Amazon. Our class returned to Manaus having learned many lessons, and it was because of that experience that many of them are particularly active in environmental issues in Brazil today. That field trip also opened my eyes to the dangers of destruction of the Amazon forest, and from that time on my research became more applied, concentrating on economic botany, the selection of forest reserves and parks, and ways in which to use the forest in more sustainable ways.

I returned to the Trans-Amazon highway on a collecting expedition in 1981 and saw that our predictions were correct: many of the farmers had left their lots and the commonest sight was abandoned cattle pasture. Instead of millions being settled in the region, only 10,000 settlers had arrived. Because of the obvious failure of the settlement programme along the highway, the next President of Brazil, President Geisel, changed the government strategy and encouraged large-scale cattle ranchers to open up the area. Large tax incentives were given to wealthy industrialists and to national and foreign companies to enable them to build cattle ranches. Cattle ranching, however, has also failed in most of the region, because the soil is so poor and because of the way it has become compacted and lost its drainage capacity through the action of the hooves of the cattle.

There have been several attempts at large-scale plantation forestry in Amazonia. These have also been a chapter of disasters! The two best-known examples are Fordlândia, a huge rubber plantation created by Henry Ford, and the Jarí Forestry Project, the dream of American multimillionaire, Daniel Ludwig.

Rubber (*Hevea brasiliensis*) is an Amazon native and, from the discovery of the process of vulcanisation that stabilised it until the turn of the century, Amazonia held the monopoly on rubber. In 1876, rubber was successfully introduced to tropical Asia and the rubber boom that had created many personal fortunes and brought prosperity to the Amazon cities of Iquitos, Manaus and Belém ended as soon as the Asian trees began to produce latex in quantity, in about 1910. Rubber grew much better in Asia, where it was far removed from its natural pests and diseases. In 1926, the Ford Motor Company decided to plant a huge rubber plantation in the Amazon. In spite of huge investment in the plantation and the town to support it, the project was a complete failure. The rubber trees were soon attacked by a number of fungal diseases that are endemic to the Amazon region but do not occur in South-east Asia, especially the leaf rust fungus, *Microcyclus ulei*. Wild rubber trees are distributed sparsely throughout the forest and thus are not so susceptible to fungal diseases because these do not spread easily from tree to tree in the species-diverse rainforest. Once the trees are clustered together in a plantation, however, the diseases spread very quickly. As a result, Henry Ford's dream of once again supplying the world with rubber from the Amazon was a disaster.

Once the forest has been cleared, the fragile Amazon soils are unprotected. The nutrients held in the topsoil are rapidly lost through leaching and wind erosion. The receding water at the end of the rainy season leaves a surface which bakes to a hard, crazed, lifeless pavement, where before the rich *várzea* (flooded forest) stood.

The Jarí Forestry project grew out of Daniel Ludwig's prediction that there would be a world shortage of paper pulp. His solution was to start a large plantation of a fast-growing relative of teak, *Gmelina arborea*. The project began in 1967 along the Jarí River, which forms the border between the Brazilian states of Pará and Amapá. Large areas of rainforest were felled and replaced by gmelina trees. Initially, clearing was carried out by bulldozers, which removed all the debris and topsoil. The trees did not grow as well as predicted because of the poor soil beneath the top soil. The strategy was changed and gangs of axemen were brought in to replace the bulldozers, so that the topsoil was left intact. The gmelina grew better amongst the debris of the former forest than it had done on bare, scraped soil. However, it was soon noted that some plantations were growing much better than others. Those on clay soils prospered but those on the sandy soils of the Guiana shield did not. The basic research that would have determined that gmelina grows on clay soils but not on sandy ones had not been done prior to planting. On areas with sandy soils, gmelina had to be replaced by Caribbean pine (*Pinus caribaea*), which is slower growing and thus changed the economics of the project. In spite of an investment of over a billion dollars (£588,250,000), Jarí has not proved economically viable. In 1982, Mr Ludwig sold out to a consortium of twenty-seven Brazilian companies which was backed by the government. His loss was $600 million (£350 million). The plantation continues to produce pulp, but only breaks even because of a deposit of kaolin clay on the property which makes a good profit.

Forestry using monoculture plantations in the Amazon has therefore not succeeded. Unlike the species-diverse agroforestry of the Indians, the large plantations are just too susceptible to disease and predators.

There are at present over half a million gold miners (*garimpeiros*) working throughout the Amazon region in a gold rush of unprecedented magnitude, with an almost equal number of diamond and tin miners adding to the problem. The *garimpeiros* are dredging the bottoms of many of the major rivers, including the territory of Indian tribes, and causing damage to the environment. Apart from the diseases they spread to the native populations, the gold miners are also causing a serious problem with mercury pollution. They use mercury to form an amalgam with the gold and then burn off the mercury. Much metallic mercury and mercury vapour escapes into the Amazon ecosystem. Many of the fish are now full of mercury, and doctors in the cities of Manaus and Santarém are frequently having to treat children who live in the cities for mercury poisoning caused by eating fish from the local markets.

The territory of the Yanomami Indians has been particularly badly affected by this activity. At one point, it was estimated that 45,000 gold miners had invaded this area. On one of my expeditions, we walked 280 kilometres through Yanomami territory from Surucucus to Uaicá on the Rio Uraricoera. We were privileged to pass through several Yanomami villages which had never been visited by westerners. Our daily routine was half a day

collecting plants, and half a day progressing through the forest by compass
bearing or on Indian trails. One evening, we arrived tired and sweaty at a
remote Yanomami village and, after the initial formalities of
greeting, we rushed off to the stream to take a bath to cool
down and get clean. Immediately some of the Indians came up
to us in obvious agitation and our translator explained that we
could not bathe here as this was the source of their drinking
water. We must bathe downstream from the village. These
people, who normally take such good care of their water
quality, have now had their streams filled with mercury and
many river banks blasted away with dynamite so that the
streams now flow with polluted and muddy water, rather than
with clear, fresh drinking-water.

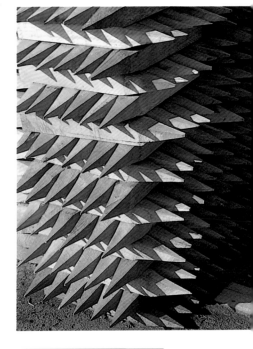

There are many other ways in which the Amazon forest is
being destroyed: to make charcoal for the pig-iron smelters
along the Carajás railway; for oil and gas mines, especially in
the upper Amazon in Ecuador; and by the flooding of new lakes
caused by hydroelectric dams. The press has done a good job of
drawing the dangers of deforestation to the attention of the
world and so there is no need to give further details here. The
most important point is that much of the deforestation so far
has been for ecologically and economically unsound uses: for
cattle pastures that are only viable because of government sub-
sidies; for timber plantations that are economic disasters; or for
hydroelectric dams such as Balbina, which produce only small
amounts of electricity yet flood huge areas of forest. It is sad
that so much deforestation has brought no long-term benefit,
either to Brazil or to the local people. The challenge for the
future is to reverse this trend and develop ways in which the
Amazon basin can be used for long-term sustainable projects.
These are much more likely to resemble the methods of the indigenous population than the farming and forestry practices

Because of the huge distances
and difficult logistics of the
Amazon, most of the noble
trees felled do not even make
their way to the export timber markets, where they
might be used in the making
of furniture. It is not uncom-
mon to find rough fencing
made out of mahogany, and
good quality hardwoods are
the norm for rough timber
construction.

familiar in the West. Today there is hope and, rather than dwell any longer on the destruction, we should look ahead and see how attitudes to the Amazon in the Amazon countries have changed dramatically over the last two or three years.

◄ The famous Serra Pelada gold mine has spawned a far more destructive litter of smaller 'holes', spread throughout the Amazon. The unsightliness of these scars is nothing compared to the less visible but far more extensive hidden environmental damage.

Water is essential in the ► gold mine. Pumped by powerful diesel engines, it is used as a weapon to cut into the soft sediment, turning it into an ochreous sludge. This is then passed down a sluice, where the gold, which is heavier than the rest, sinks to the bottom. The process is inefficient; over 60 per cent of the gold is washed away with the sediment.

◄ The Amazon is built on its river system, but uncontrolled mining by privateer prospectors, or *garimpeiros*, is having a profound effect on the rivers. On the Rio Madeira, over 2000 crudely constructed dredgers, each with a huge diesel-driven pump, churn up the river bed in search of gold (opposite, top). The river has been turned into a milky sludge for thousands of kilometres, killing fish and animals, and endangering the lives of the forest people. The *garimpeiros* use enormous quantities of mercury (bottom left) to purify the gold. Because of the crudeness of the process, tons of the highly toxic metal are being released into the environment, where it is readily absorbed into the food chain. Mercury poisoning is fast becoming a major cause of illness in the Brazilian Amazon. It is estimated that as much as 80 to 90 per cent of the gold produced (bottom right) is exported illegally. Brazil suffers the environmental cost of extracting the metal, but reaps little of the financial benefit.

▲ Immigration into the Amazon is relentless. Roads built to give access for logging or oil exploration encourage an influx of settlers. Many of these come from the south, bringing with them agricultural methods inappropriate to the Amazon. Their crops inevitably fail, forcing them to move on. The land they leave behind becomes degraded scrub, with low species diversity. Reforestation of these areas does not readily occur naturally.

Large-scale cattle ranching came to the Amazon on the back of huge government financial incentives. Bulldozers are used to fell the forest, which is dried and burned. The grass planted on the cleared land becomes poor and infested with weeds within a few years, the poor soil becomes compacted, and what little nutrients are present are rapidly lost in the increased run-off of rain water. Such ranches, many occupying thousands of hectares, are neither financially nor environmentally viable from an agricultural standpoint.

The huge Carajás mine, whose railhead stockpile is shown here (above), is highly mechanised and carefully controlled. Most of the ore is exported via the 890-kilometre railway to the coast. Although direct environmental damage is limited, the mine and railway have brought privately owned smelting plants fired by charcoal (right); the charcoal comes from felled virgin rainforest. Poorly controlled development attracted by the mine is accelerating the already rapid deforestation of the State of Pará.

The commonest method for clearing forest is to cut down the majority of the trees, leaving the largest and hardest standing. This is done at the end of the wet season. The felled forest is left through the dry season, and is then set on fire during June and July. At this time of year, the pall of smoke can be so extensive that city airports have to be closed. Often, not even the most valuable timber is removed and sold, so the wealth of the forest merely goes up in smoke.

Only about 15 per cent of the Amazon forest has been destroyed so far, but the threats described here could result in clearance on an accelerating scale through the coming decades. Climatologists believe that if a substantial area of the eastern Amazon (shown here) is cleared, the recycling of water across the forest from the Atlantic Ocean to the Andes, which depends on the trees and plants, may suffer a catastrophic interruption. This would result in the drying out of the forest further to the west, and its destruction by fire and desiccation.

NINE

Reconstruction: a Ray of Hope

The destruction of natural ecosystems in the Amazon is a cause for concern. However, in the Brazilian Amazon, up to 1990, only about 420,000 square kilometres had been completely destroyed; that is, approximately 8.5 per cent of the total area of the legal Amazon. Deforestation in Amazonian Brazil in 1987 was a great cause for concern because it was over 40,000 square kilometres. However, because of changes in government policy, this figure was reduced to 18,842 square kilometres in 1988 and to 13,818 square kilometres in 1989. Deforestation has not stopped but it has definitely slowed down. A much larger area of the Amazon forest has been disturbed in some way, such as by excess removal of useful tree species, for example, mahogany and rosewood, and also by over-hunting of many animals, such as jaguar, turtles and caymans. Nevertheless, with 90 per cent of the Amazon forest more or less intact, there is still room for hope that wise conservation policies and sustainable methods of utilisation can be worked out before it is too late. It seems appropriate, therefore, to end with some of the signs that lessons are being learned from the failures to develop the region rationally, and that there is now new hope for the future of the Amazon.

Indian children learn about their intricate and complex system of crop management at an early age; their schoolroom is the village garden.

The decrease in the rate of deforestation in the Brazilian Amazon is the result of a complete change in government policy as the country has moved from a military to an elected form of government. The plea of many Brazilian voters to save the rainforests is now being heeded. Instead of giving tax incentives for cattle farms, the government is tracing forest fires by means of satellite images and fining farmers who cut down the forest illegally. The commitment of the current Brazilian government to the environment is shown by the fact that José Lutzenberger, Brazil's leading environmental activist, who campaigned for the forest and its peoples for many years, was the first Special Secretary for the Environment in the cabinet of President Collor de Mello. During his appointment, Lutzenberger worked ceaselessly to improve the environmental record of Brazil, and he succeeded in no small measure.

The transition from military dictatorships to democracy which has occurred in Latin America has been no less fundamental than the change from communism which is occurring in Eastern Europe. It would have been inconceivable only a few years ago that Dr José Lutzenberger, then the most vociferous and outspoken critic of the Brazilian government's environmental record, would join the government.

For more than twenty years, human rights organisations, anthropologists and many other people in Brazil and abroad have been campaigning for the creation of a large reserve to protect the Yanomami Indians, the least acculturated of the few remaining large tribes of Indians. The Indians themselves, under the leadership of Davi Kopenawa, have also sought recognition of their territory. I remember talking to Davi about his people in 1984 when he acted as my field guide on an expedition to the top of Pico Rondon in Yanomami territory. He was our guide because of his fluency in Portuguese. He repeatedly exhorted us, 'When you leave our territory, please do not forget the Yanomami people; help us to gain our land.' It was not long after this that I began to read in the international press about Davi's activities. When he visited the Royal Botanic Gardens, Kew, in 1990, I proudly showed him our rainforest in the Princess of Wales Conservatory. Instead of the expected reaction of pleasure, I received another lesson in Indian thought. He said, 'This stream has nowhere to go; the trees are prisoners under this glass. The forest and the streams must be free to wander where they like.'

Davi Kopenawa's courageous work for his people has been rewarded. On 15 November 1991, against considerable opposition from the military, some state governors and various developers, President Collor signed a decree for the demarcation of 9,419,108 hectares as the Yanomami Reserve. This directive handed over permanent rights to the Indians in their land, an area three times the size of

Belgium. The Yanomami decree was quickly followed by another recognising 4,913,000 hectares of the states of Pará and Mato Grosso for the Menkranotire Indians, a branch of the Kayapó.

After five centuries of persecution, the Indians are gaining the recognition of their rights throughout the Amazon region. In 1989, President Barco of Colombia set aside over 50 per cent of the Colombian Amazon as an area for the indigenous peoples. The Indians are also well protected in Amazonian Venezuela, and Bolivia has recognised 2 million hectares as indigenous property. Perhaps those of the Indians who are left will fare better than those who belonged to the many tribes which became extinct in the earlier part of this century.

Prior to declaring the Yanomami Reserve, the Brazilian government also worked hard to exclude gold miners from the territory, and have succeeded to a large measure. Government action included the dynamiting of many of the clandestine airstrips in Yanomami territory. It will, however, take a long time for the population to recover from the ravages of all the western diseases and pollution introduced by the miners.

Some of the large mining companies operating in Amazonia are also taking a responsible stand on environmental issues. In 1989, I made an interesting visit to a bauxite mine on the Trombetas River, just north of the main Amazon River in Pará State in Brazil. The mining company was quite honest in admitting some earlier environmental mistakes during the initial phase of the project: the staff showed me a landslide caused by mining too near the edge of the plateau, and their lake for tailings, which had once flooded into the Trombetas. Apart from correcting these mistakes, what impressed me most was their reforestation project, which has been under way since the beginning of the mine under the guidance of their staff ecologist, Oliver Henry Knowles. He was using about ninety native species of trees for planting, and was creating a good succession from secondary forest coloniser species to primary forest.

This programme of restoration is successful because the mine was prepared to spend $2,500 (£1,475) per hectare to ensure that the area is not left bare. That mine has control over a large area of forest, 10 per cent of which will be destroyed by the mining process. The rest is rigorously guarded as a forest reserve. Because hunting is strictly controlled in that area, it is full of animals such as jaguar, capybara and deer, which have become rare throughout much of the region. The Mineração Rio do Norte mine is not alone in caring for the forest, but it is a leading example for other mining operations in the region, and had embarked on the process of reforestation long before most other mines had thought of it. There is also, for example, an extensive environmental programme attached to the Carajás iron mine. That concern needs to spread to the areas beyond the control of the company operating the mine, to where pig-iron is being smelted between the mine and the coast.

Another hope for the forest is the extensive work being carried out on sustainable ways in which to use it. Several extractive reserves have been created in the States of Acre and Amapá for the local people to use for the gathering of forest products. So far, extraction has been based mainly on rubber and Brazil nuts, and yields a meagre existence for the gatherers. Many people, such as Jason Clay, anthropologist of Cultural Survival, and Anita Roddick of the Body Shop, are striving to improve the situation by creating a market for a larger range of forest products and by developing more direct access to markets, without a long chain of middlemen. Those products with most potential are oils and fragrances for use in cosmetics, and flavours and fruits for use by the food industry. I have been working with a food company to introduce cupuaçú and açaí ice-creams as a rainforest flavour in the United Kingdom. Extraction will not solve the entire problem of the Amazon basin but, together with the sustainable agroforestry type of farming, the use of richer soils, controlled extraction of timber, and the development of a more environmentally conscious mining programme, there are distinct possibilities that the Amazon basin can be both productive and a continued home for its diversity of plant and animal species and of indigenous cultures and other forest people.

These are some of the hopeful signs in Amazonia, but we should not relax the pressure at this stage. There is still a strong lobby against conservation, against indigenous cultures and against rational development. While the federal government of Brazil is strongly in favour of a rational policy for Amazonia, there are many interests against this. For example, several state governors of the region have campaigned for elections and succeeded on distinctly anti-environmental platforms. The military is also worried about leaving areas of Amazonia unoccupied and is keen to promote paranoia about internationalisation of the region. Part of the future work on developing the Amazon must include contact with these groups and, especially, convincing the military that there is no international desire to challenge the sovereignty of any of the Amazon nations.

I entered the Amazon rainforest in 1963 as an enthusiastic young post-doctoral botanist, ready to cut down trees in order to collect a few pressed herbarium specimens for study. However, I soon learned from the peoples of the forest, such as Frederick the Djuka in Suriname mentioned in chapter 1 of this book, of the value which they place upon a single tree. Over the intervening period of almost three decades the world environment has deteriorated badly and awareness of the seriousness of this problem has heightened. At the same time, I have learned a great deal more about the way the forest works, the diversity of organisms that it contains, the intricate network of inter-relationships that binds them all together, the number of potentially useful natural products which are available, and the function that the forest performs to maintain the stability of the world environment. This has convinced me that the destruction of the Amazon rainforest would be a tragedy which future generations would never forgive.

Davi Kopenawa Yanomami is a persuasive speaker on behalf of his people. The Yanomami have had a relatively short exposure to 'mainstream' Brazilian culture, but Davi has had a huge impact wherever he has spoken. His dignified pleas for help for his people, and his straightforward condemnation of industrial man's destruction of the environment are difficult to ignore.

The lives of the 10,000 or so Brazilian Yanomami have been devastated by the arrival of 40,000 *garimpeiro* invaders. They brought disease and poisoning, destroyed the Yanomami's food sources, and damaged the Indian culture. The government of Brazil, despite strong opposition, sent in forces to remove the *garimpeiros*, and decreed the demarcation of all of the Yanomami land. In a high-profile campaign, 'Operation Popcorn', the army used dynamite to destroy many of the hundred or so clandestine airstrips built to supply the gold mines. Military action has continued at a lower level, and it is now reckoned that less than 2000 *garimpeiros* remain. As long as the government continues to police the area, there is hope for the survival of the Yanomami people and their culture.

On the Trombetas River, the tailings (a suspension of sludge from washing the ore) from a huge bauxite mine used to drain into a natural lake, which overflowed, polluting the river. Nowadays, the children of company employees paddle in the lake; the tailings are now channelled instead into a purpose-made system of settlement lagoons.

The rainfall and climatic pattern of the Amazon will be changed if a significant proportion of the tree cover is lost. But there are signs that the harsh lessons learnt in Africa and the Far East are being heeded by Brazil; at the Trombetas bauxite mine, a substantial and so far successful programme of reforestation has been operating for more than five years in areas where mining has been completed. The new trees are native species, and it is hoped that the new forest will be recolonised by animals and plants from the surrounding undisturbed areas.

The forest people are becoming increasingly adept at marshalling both Brazilian and foreign public opinion to support them in their battle against destructive development. Raoni, a chief of the Kayapó, toured the world to raise support for the demarcation of Kayapó territory. He was also an important figure in the Altamira Assembly of Indian Nations, which persuaded the World Bank to withdraw support for a series of dams which would flood huge areas of Indian land. The repercussions went much further; the world at last realised that tribal leaders had significant and persuasive arguments against development projects, which they could put across in a most eloquent and forceful way.

◄ In the Xingu Indian Park, Kayapó villages are entering the international market economy. In partnership with the Body Shop, they are collecting Brazil nuts for use in toiletries. They extract the oil in their villages, and sell direct to the Body Shop, thus deriving a far higher income. This press was developed in conjunction with ICI – a good example of 'appropriate technology'.

▲ The Body Shop is in business; although founder Anita Roddick believes in 'ethical trading', the company is profitable, and it is profitable largely because its customers believe in its ethical trading policies. Unlike the managing directors of most other major companies, Anita spends a proportion of her time visiting her suppliers, especially when they live deep in the Brazilian forest!

Brasília, in the heart of Brazil was planned in the 1950s by architects Lúcio Costa and Oscar Niemeyer for the then president, Juscelino Kubitschek. It was intended as a focus for the development of the Amazon. Had this succeeded there would be little forest remaining in Brazil today. However, the incumbent president is adopting a more responsible approach to the Amazon than his predecessors. Brasília, symbolic of the environmentally destructive power of mankind, may yet come to represent a positive approach to development.